For my very special love

From

Other books in this series:
Best Friends
Thank you Mum
Have a Perfect Day
My Dad, My Hero
Stay Calm

Published in 2010 by Helen Exley Giftbooks in Great Britain. A copy of the CIP data is available from the British Library on request. All rights reserved. No part of this publication may be reproduced or transmitted in any form or by any means, electronic or mechanical, including photocopy, recording or any information storage and retrieval system without permission in writing from the Publisher.
Printed in China.

Words and illustrations © Jenny Kempe 2010
Design and arrangement © Exley Publications 2010
The moral right of the author has been asserted.

12 11 10 9 8 7 6 5 4 3 2

ISBN: 978-1-84634-490-9

Dedication: To everybody who knows how to fall head over heels. And to Keith, my love.

Published by HELEN EXLEY®
Helen Exley Giftbooks, 16 Chalk Hill, Watford, Herts WD19 4BG, UK.
www.helenexleygiftbooks.com

I've got a crush
on you

WORDS AND ILLUSTRATIONS BY

JENNY KEMPE

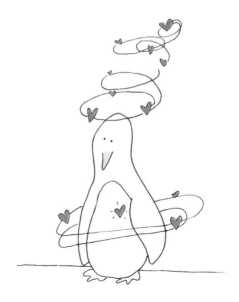

It's like a runaway snowball.

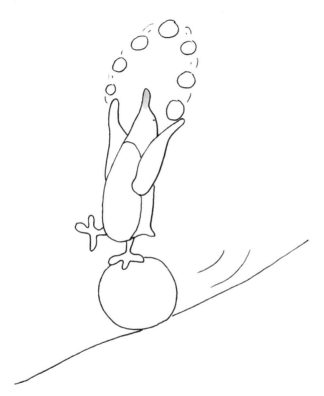

It started and now it won't stop.

I can't eat.
I can't sleep.

I'm finding it a little
hard to focus.

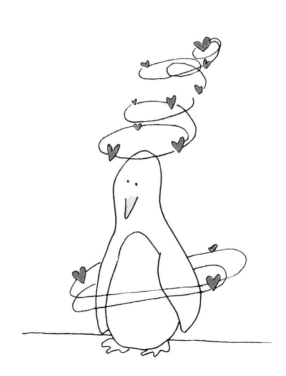

I've taken a fresh interest
in my appearance.

I've got heaps of creativity.

I live for the moment.

I'm really, really happy to be alive!

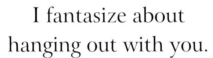

I fantasize about
hanging out with you.

I take every opportunity
to let the world know
how fantastic and truly unique
you are.

I am keen to create
a lasting impression.

When you look at me,

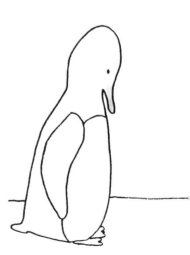

I feel weak.

I find the things you say
deeply fascinating.

If you touch me, I tremble.

If you kiss me, I melt.

And do you know why
I feel the way I do?

It's all because
I've got an irrevocable,
up-to-the-stars-and-down-
to-the-ground
Massive Crush!

I am madly in

love with you

Jenny Kempe

In 2009, overwhelmed by the endless bad news in the media, Jenny Kempe decided to take a six month break from newspapers, TV and radio. She turned her focus to the things in life that made her happy; to friends and family and to "taking time to just be". The result is the wonderfully bright and positive gift book series "Life is Beautiful". Each title has been designed to warm your heart and to put a smile on your face. As gifts, these books will brighten up the day, or even the life, of someone you care for.

About Helen Exley gifts

Helen Exley products cover the most powerful range of all
human relationships: love between couples, the bonds within
families and between friends. No expense is spared in making
sure that each book is as thoughtful and meaningful a gift
as it is possible to create: good to give, good to receive.
You have the result in your hands. If you have loved it –
tell others!

Visit our website to see all of Helen Exley's other books
and gifts: **www.helenexleygiftbooks.com**

Helen Exley Giftbooks
16 Chalk Hill, Watford, Herts
WD19 4BG, UK
www.helenexleygiftbooks.com

We loved making this book for you.
We hope you'll enjoy the other titles
in our series Life is Beautiful.

The Life is Beautiful Team